Tony Goes Shopping

Written by Valerie Sheehan

Illustrated by Susan Meaney

For Grace

Tony opens his eyes and stretches out wide.

He hears Mummy calling him and decides to hide.

Mum comes upstairs with a smile on her face,
"Oh no, where's Tony?
Has he flown off to space?"

Just then the blankets begin to wiggle,
and Mum is sure she hears a giggle.

Out **pops** Tony from his hiding place,
with a **big grin** on his little face!

Mum makes Tony **laugh** as only she can.
They go downstairs to check the day plan.

Having a day plan helps the day run smoothly,
Tony feels safe and isn't so moody.

It's hard for Tony to find the words he should say,
when things don't always go his way.

Sometimes it's **easier** to hide in his shell
and stay in there until he feels **well.**

I don't like surprises

Tony **listens** to Mum and to Dad,
they help him out of his shell, when he feels sad.

Tony's sister Tess is already downstairs,

"Come on," says Mum "up on your chairs.

"Let's eat our breakfast, then we shall see what's on the day plan before TV."

When Mum said shopping, Tony's face **fell**,
he tried to **retreat** into his shell.

"**Out you come** Tony and listen to me,
FIRST we go shopping, THEN watch TV."

"Shopping in five minutes!"
Mum calls from upstairs.

Tony and Tess crawl off their chairs.

Tony likes a time warning, it helps him be ready.
Out to the car they go, slow and steady.

Wow the supermarket is bright, it hurts Tony's eyes there is so much light.

It's too noisy!

50%

SALE!

½ PRICE!

2 FOR 1

The noise all around him hurts his ears, and brings poor Tony close to tears.

Once again he **retreats** to his shell,
but Mum has a game to make him feel well.

"Here is a list
just for you.

You must find
three things,
here's a clue.

"One thing gets hot, while one is cold,
the other **smells nice** and is heavy to hold."

Tony is so busy playing Mum's special game,
he forgets the noise and is glad he came.

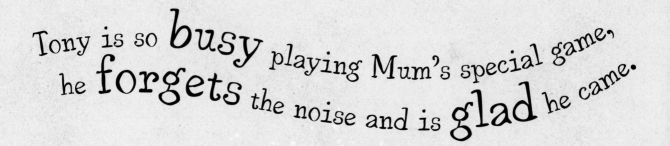

Walking slowly along with Mum and Tess,
Tony is happy so he worries less.

When Mum stops to chat to someone she knows,
Tony feels anxious and wants to go.

Everyone speaks too quickly

Mum tells Tony not to worry,
she is just saying hello and she will hurry.

"If someone says hello Tony,
we look in their eyes.

It makes no difference, what their size!

"It's always nice to be polite,
I know you can do it, because it's right."

Then it's time to queue up at the till,
Tony doesn't like it when he
has to stand still.

Tony began to feel agitated
but mum had a plan for them while they waited.

Mum tells Tony to COUNT the trollies he can see, while Tess counts the people one, two, three.

Everything in now, except the ham. "Keep counting Tony it helps you stay calm."

Back in the car, the shopping complete,
it's time to go home and **rest their feet.**

Everyone is **happy** as shopping went well,
and Tony managed to **stay out** of his shell.

Who can remember what's **next** on the plan!
Can Tony watch TV now?

Yes He Can!